The Original WARM FUZZY TALE

A FAIRYTALE

BY

Claude Steiner

with pictures by

JoAnn Dick

Published by

JALMAR PRESS INC.

SACRAMENTO

Copyright© 1977 by JALMAR Press, Inc.

ISBN — 0-915190-08-7 Library of Congress 77-77981

Decorative Lettering by Penny Nugent

2nd Printing June 1978 — 25,000
1st Printing May 1977 — 25,000

JALMAR Press, Inc.
6501 Elvas Ave.
Sacramento, CA 95819
(916) 451-2897

To Eric and Mimi, my two children,
whose love shaped and is shaped by this story.

Once upon a time, a long time ago, there lived two very happy people called Tim and Maggi....

...with their two children,
John and Lucy.

To understand how happy they were, you have to understand how things were in those days.

You see, in those happy days everyone was given at birth a small, soft Fuzzy Bag. Anytime a person reached into this bag he was able to pull out a Warm Fuzzy.

arm Fuzzies were very much in demand because whenever somebody was given a Warm Fuzzy it made him feel warm and fuzzy all over.

eople who didn't get Warm Fuzzies regularly were in danger of developing a sickness in their backs which caused them to shrivel up and die.

n those days it was very easy to get Warm Fuzzies. Anytime that somebody felt like it, he might walk up to you and say, "I'd like to have a Warm Fuzzy."

Thank you!

You would then reach into your bag and pull out a Fuzzy the size of a little girl's hand. As soon as the Fuzzy saw the light of day it would smile and blossom into a large, shaggy Warm Fuzzy.

You then would lay it on the person's shoulder or head or lap and it would snuggle up and melt right against their skin and make them feel good all over.

People were always asking each other for Warm Fuzzies, and since they were always given freely, getting enough of them was never a problem.

There were always plenty to go
around, and as a consequence
everyone was happy and felt warm
and fuzzy
most of the
time.

One day a bad witch became angry
because everyone was so happy and
no one was buying potions and salves.

he witch was very clever and devised a very wicked plan.

One beautiful morning the witch crept up to Tim while Maggi was playing with their daughter and whispered in his ear, "See here, Tim, look at all the Fuzzies that Maggi is giving to Lucy. You know, if she keeps it up, eventually she is going to run out and then there won't be any left for you."

Tim was astonished. He turned to the witch and said, "Do you mean to tell me that there isn't a Warm Fuzzy in our bag every time we reach into it?"

Hope some people fall for the boss' new wicked plan. We need the business!

And the witch said, "No, absolutely not, and once you run out, that's it. You don't have any more." With this, the witch flew away, laughing and cackling.

Tim took this to heart and began to notice every time. Maggi gave up a Warm Fuzzy to somebody else. Eventually he got very worried and upset because he liked Maggi's Warm Fuzzies very much and did not want to give them up. He certainly did not think it was right for Maggi to be spending all her Warm Fuzzies on the children and on other people.

He began to complain every time he saw Maggi giving a Warm Fuzzy to somebody else, and because Maggi liked him very much, she stopped giving Warm Fuzzies to other people as often and reserved them for him.

Tim looks upset!

The witche's plan must be working.

The children watched this and soon began to get the idea that it was wrong to give up Warm Fuzzies any time you were asked or felt like it.

They too became very careful. They would watch their parents closely, and whenever they felt that one of their parents was giving too many Fuzzies to others, they also began to object. They began to feel worried whenever they gave away too many Warm Fuzzies.

Phew! What's cooking?

Must be brewing newts again!

Even though they found a Warm Fuzzy every time they reached into their bag, they reached in less and less and became more and more stingy. Soon people began to notice the lack of Warm Fuzzies, and they began to feel less warm and less fuzzy. They began to shrivel up, and, occasionally, people would die from lack of Warm Fuzzies.

More and more people went to the witch to buy potions and salves even though they didn't seem to work.

Well, the situation was getting very serious indeed. The bad witch didn't really want the people to die (since dead people couldn't buy salves and potions) so a new plan was devised.

Everyone was given a bag that was very similar to the Fuzzy Bag except that this one was cold while the Fuzzy Bag was warm. Inside of the witch's bag were Cold Pricklies. These Cold Pricklies did not make people feel warm and fuzzy, but made them feel cold and prickly instead.

ut they did prevent peoples' backs from shriveling up. So, from then on, everytime somebody said, "I want a Warm Fuzzy," people who were worried about depleting their supply would say, "I can't give you a Warm Fuzzy, but would you like a Cold Prickly?"

Sometimes, two people would walk up to each other, thinking they could get a Warm Fuzzy, but one or the other of them would change his mind and they would wind up giving each other Cold Pricklies. So while very few people were dying, a lot of people were still unhappy and feeling very cold and Prickly.

The situation got very complicated. Warm Fuzzies, which used to be thought of as free as air, became extremely valuable.

This caused people to do all sorts of things in order to obtain them.

Before the witch had appeared, people used to gather in groups of three or four or five, never caring too much who was giving Warm Fuzzies to whom. After the coming of the witch, people began to pair off and to reserve all their Warm Fuzzies for each other exclusively. People who forgot themselves and gave a Fuzzy to someone else would feel guilty because they knew that their partner would probably resent the loss. People who could not find a generous partner had to buy their Fuzzies and they worked long hours to earn the money.

27

Another thing which happened was that some people would take Cold Pricklies --- which were limitless and freely available --- coat them white and fluffy, and pass them on as Warm Fuzzies.

These counterfeit Warm Fuzzies were really Plastic Fuzzies, and they caused additional difficulties. For instance, two people would get together and freely exchange Plastic Fuzzies, which presumably should have made them feel good, but they came away feeling bad instead. Since they thought they had been exchanging Warm Fuzzies, people grew very confused about this, never realizing that their cold, prickly feelings were really the result of the fact that they had been given a lot of Plastic Fuzzies.

Plastic Fuzzies?

It looks like a Warm Fuzzy.

Ouch! But it's not.

So the situation was very, very dismal, and it all started because of the coming of the witch who made people believe that some day, when least expected, they might reach into their Warm Fuzzy Bag and find no more.

No! No! I can't give you any more Warm Fuzzies!. I've run out!

No! No!

toss turn toss turn

Not long ago, a lovely, strong woman with big hips and a happy smile came to this unhappy land.

She seemed not to have heard about the witch and was not worried about running out of Warm Fuzzies.

She gave them out freely, even when not asked. People called her the Hip Woman and some disapproved of her because she was giving the children the idea that they should not worry about running out of Warm Fuzzies.

Oh oh! The boss won't like that!

What a nice lady! Look! She's giving Warm Fuzzies!

That bad cat needs a Warm Fuzzy!

The children liked her very much because they felt good around her. They, too, began to give out Warm Fuzzies whenever they felt like it.

he grownups became concerned and
decided to pass a law to protect the
children from using up their
supplies of Warm Fuzzies. The law
made it a criminal offense to give out
Warm Fuzzies in a reckless manner,
without a license.

any children, however, seemed not to know or care, and in spite of the law they continued to give each other Warm Fuzzies whenever they felt like it and always when asked.

ecause there were many many
children --- almost as many as
grownups --- it began to look as if
maybe the children would have
their way.

As of now it is hard to say what will happen. Will the forces of law and order stop the children? Are the grownups going to join with the Hip Woman and the children in taking a chance that there will always be as many Warm Fuzzies as needed?

Will Tim and Maggi, recalling the days when they were so happy and when Warm Fuzzies were unlimited, begin to give away Warm Fuzzies freely again?

The struggle spread all over the land and is probably going on right where you live. If you want to, and I hope you do, you can join by freely giving and asking for Warm Fuzzies and by being as loving and healthy as you can.

That cat is O.K.

THE Warm Fuzzy CLUB

All those in favor of feeling OK and feeling loved are WARM FUZZY people. The WARM FUZZY CLUB is dedicated to keeping WARM FUZZIES alive and bouncing. You can get more WARM FUZZIES and be a WARM FUZZY person to friends and family by being a WARM FUZZY CLUB MEMBER.

When you sign up for the WARM FUZZY CLUB you get your WARM FUZZY CLUB Membership Certificate and a WARM FUZZY to wear proudly. WARM FUZZY CLUB members will receive a free WARM FUZZY; I'm OK full color poster (18" x 24"). This colorful poster has the wonderful Today, I'm OK poem reprinted from TA for TOTS. The beautiful poster is ringed by all the funny lovable characters from Dr. Freed's books.

Then, every two months there's a WARM FUZZY CLUB NEWS. The NEWS is written by Dr. Alvyn M. Freed, psychologist, lecturer and author of TA for TOTS, TA for KIDS, and TA for TEENS. Dr. and Mrs. Freed (Marge) will tell you how to be happier and how to make other people happier with winning WARM FUZZY ways.

Songs of the Warm Fuzzy

All About Your Feelings
a new LP Record Album — $5.95

Entertaining fun songs inspired by the best-selling book, TA for TOTS. Helps kids get along with kids. Brings parents and kids closer. Sample songs: Hitting is Harmful — Being Scared — When I'm Angry — Warm Fuzzy Song — Why Don't Parents Say What They Mean — I'm Not Perfect (Nobody's Perfect).

TA for TOTS COLORING BOOK
$1.95

24 pages with delightful cartoon characters from TA for TOTS. Fun to color. Fun captions with messages for pre-school to 4th grade youngsters.

WARM FUZZY Today I'M OK POSTER
$1.95

Full Color Poster features the delightful cartoon characters from TA for TOTS. 18" x 24".

WARM FUZZIES

Rollicking eyes and paddle feet. Ideal for home, classroom or meeting.
50¢ each.
Minimum order 50 at 50¢ ea.
(Less than 50 — 60¢ ea.)

"LOVE IS A WARM FUZZY" T-SHIRT

Youth S-M-L-XL ... **$4.95**
Adults S-M-L-XL... **$5.95**

JALMAR PRESS INC.
6501 ELVAS AVENUE
SACRAMENTO, CA 95819
(916) 451-2897

THE WARM FUZZY COMPANY™

SHIP TO: _____

STREET _____

CITY _____ STATE _____ ZIP _____

**CHECK, MONEY ORDER, OR PURCHASE ORDER
MUST ACCOMPANY YOUR ORDER**

ORDER FORM

ORDER	AVAILABLE NOW	RETAIL	TOTAL
	BOOKS — Perfect Bound		
	TA for Tots — A. Freed	$ 5.95	
	TA for Tots (Hardback) — A. Freed	11.95	
	TA for Kids (3rd edition — revised) — A. Freed & M. Freed	4.95	
	TA for Teens (and other important people) — A. Freed	7.95	
	TA for Tots Coloring Book — A Freed	1.95	
	TA for Management — Novey	6.95	
	The Warm Fuzzy Tale — Steiner	2.95	
	Joy of Backpacking — Look	5.95	
	A Time to Teach, A Time to Dance — M. Freed	14.95	
	SPECIAL TA MATERIALS		
	Becoming the Way We Are — Levin	2.50	
	Introduce Yourself to TA — Campos & McCormick	1.25	
	Introduce Your Marriage to TA — Campos & McCormick	1.50	
	TA Made Simple — Steiner	1.00	
	The OK Game	9.95	
	Warm Fuzzy T-Shirt		
	Youth S-M-L-XL	4.95	
	Adult S-M-L-XL	5.95	
	Warm Fuzzy Club Membership	4.00	
	COMING: SPECIAL NEW TITLES		
	Warm Fuzzy Songbook — Bird	2.95 Tent.	
	Hidden Treasures (TA in the Church) — Geiger	6.95 Tent.	

ORDER	SPECIAL NEW TITLES	RETAIL	TOTAL
	Reach for the Sky (Hang gliding) — Severance	7.95	
	The Parent Book — Bessell & Kelly	9.95	
	A/V MULTIMEDIA PAC'S		
	KID-PAC—**NEW** A/V PAC Based on TA for Kids	115.00	
	TOT-PAC ( )filmstrips ( )slides (add $15.00 for slides)	135.00	
	Parent-PAC ( )record ( )cassette	19.95	
	CASSETTES, RECORDS, POSTERS		
	TA for Tots 55 minute Cassette	9.95	
	TA for Tots LP 2 Record Album Set	9.95	
	TA for Kids 45 minute Cassette	9.95	
	TA for Teens 45 minute Cassette	9.95	
	Songs of the Warm Fuzzy LP Album (all about your feelings) — Bird	5.95	
	Relax for Health Cassettes — A. Freed		
	Side A—Introduction to Hypnosis Side B—Induction, Weight Control	9.95	
	Side A—Introduction to Hypnosis Side B—Induction, Tobacco Control	9.95	
	Side A—Introduction to Hypnosis Side B—Induction, Will Power Strengthening	9.95	
	Warm Fuzzy I'm OK 4 color Poster	1.95	
	Warm Fuzzies (min. order 50)	.50 each	
	TA Growth and Development Chart — Levin	.95	
	Subtotal		
	CA Residents Add 6% Sales Tax		
	Add Shipping/handling		
(Minimum order $5.00) Total			

**Please enroll me as a member of WARM FUZZY CLUB. Enclosed
is my annual dues for Club ($4.00).**

NAME: _____

STREET: _____

CITY: _____ STATE: _____ ZIP: _____

MAIL TO: JALMAR PRESS INC.
         6501 ELVAS AVE.
         SACRAMENTO, CA 95819